A Ca...

By Liza Charlesworth

ISBN: 978-1-339-02660-2

Art Director: Tannaz Fassihi; Designer: Tanya Chernyak
Photos © Getty Images.
Copyright © Liza Charlesworth. All rights reserved. Published by Scholastic Inc.

3 4 5 6 7 8 9 10   68   32 31 30 29 28 27 26 25 24

Printed in Jiaxing, China. First printing, August 2023.

A kid has a cat.

A cat is a fun pal.

A cat can sit in a lap.

A cat can get in a bag.

A cat can get in a hat.

Can a cat get a pat?
Yes!

Can a cat nap on a mat?
Yes!

A cat is a fun pal.